The Āce's Alphabet

Created by Jay Kim

for Lilybet
(and you!)

www.jaykimbooks.us

follow @jaykimbooks

ISBN: 979-8-9870765-1-4

homophone

ho·mo·phone (noun)

> :1 of 2 or more words pronounced alike but different in meaning, spelling or derivation (like the words two, to and too)

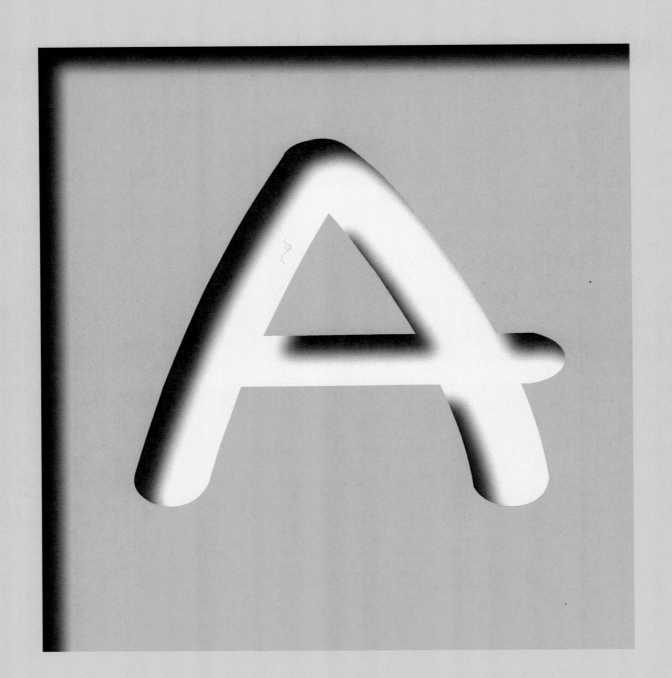

B is for Bat

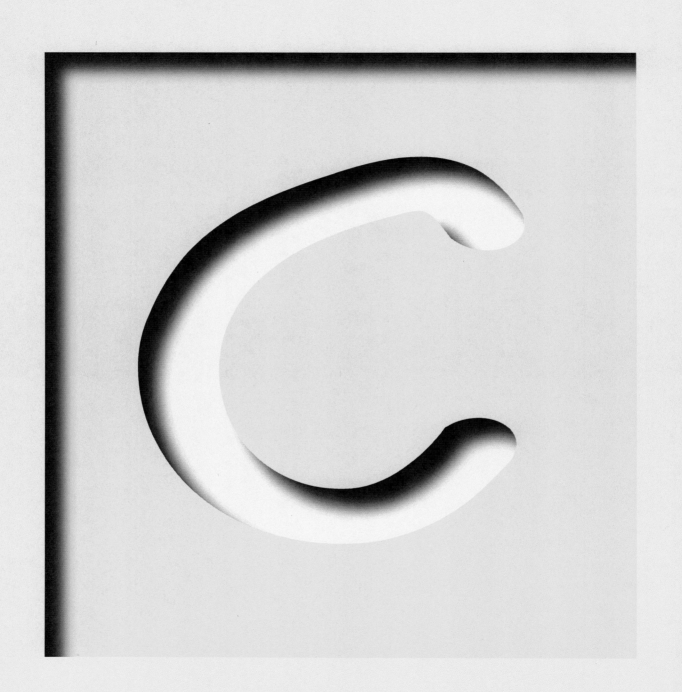

C is
for
Crane

E is for ear

G is for Glider

H is for Hotdog

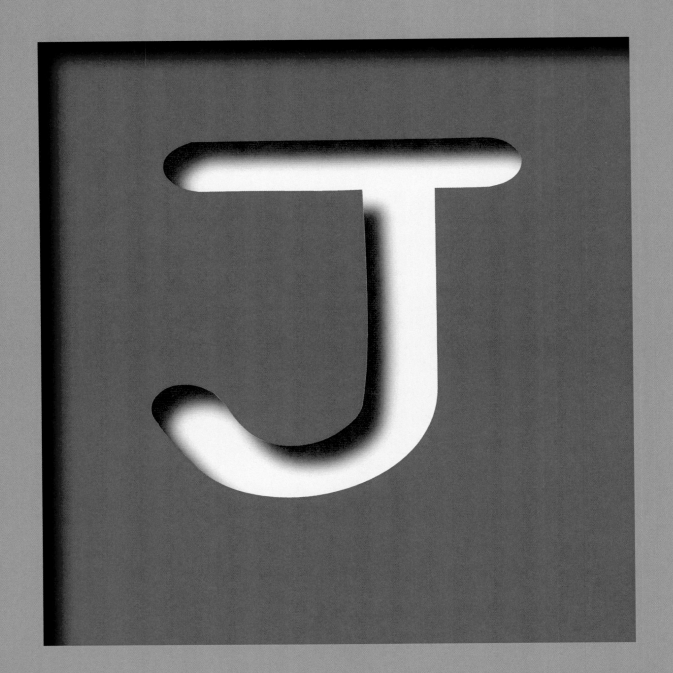

J is for Jam

L is for Lab

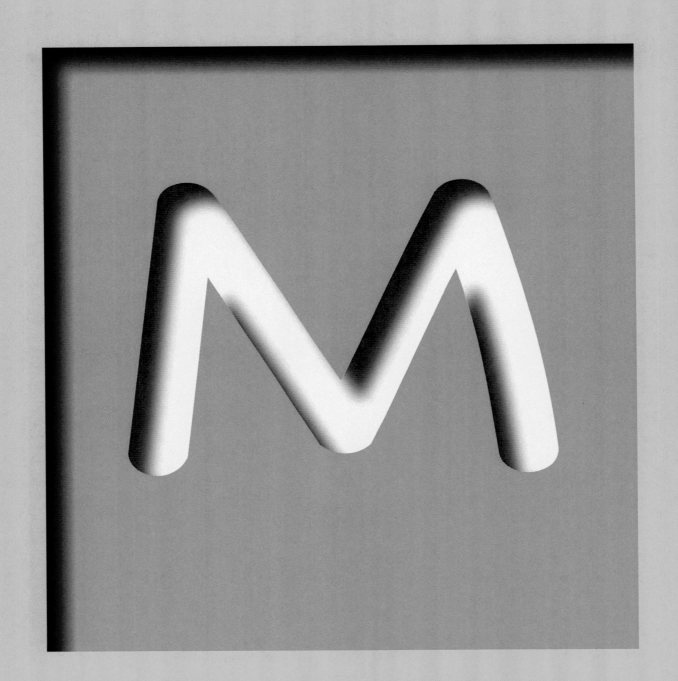

M is for Meat

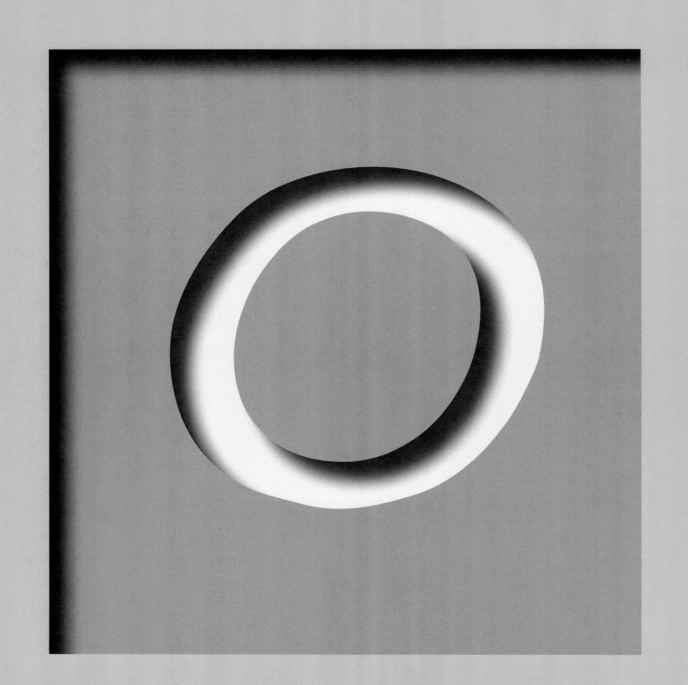

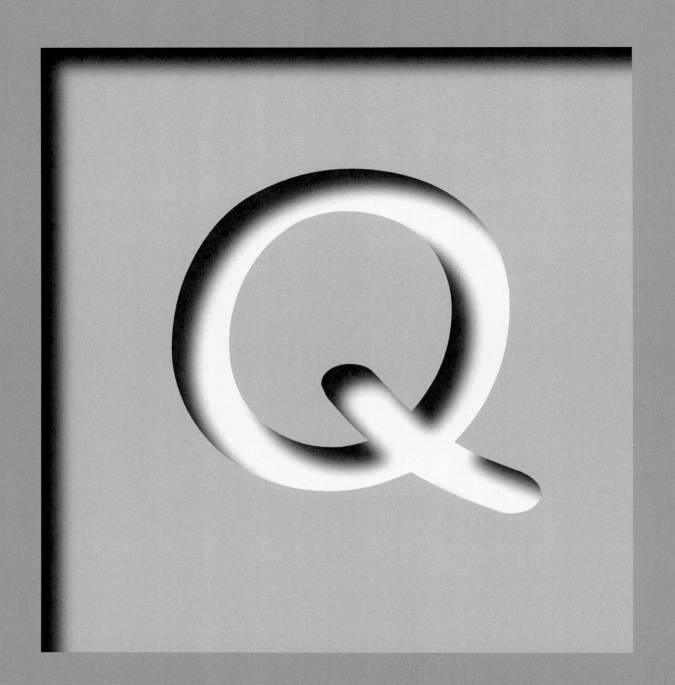

Q is for Quarter

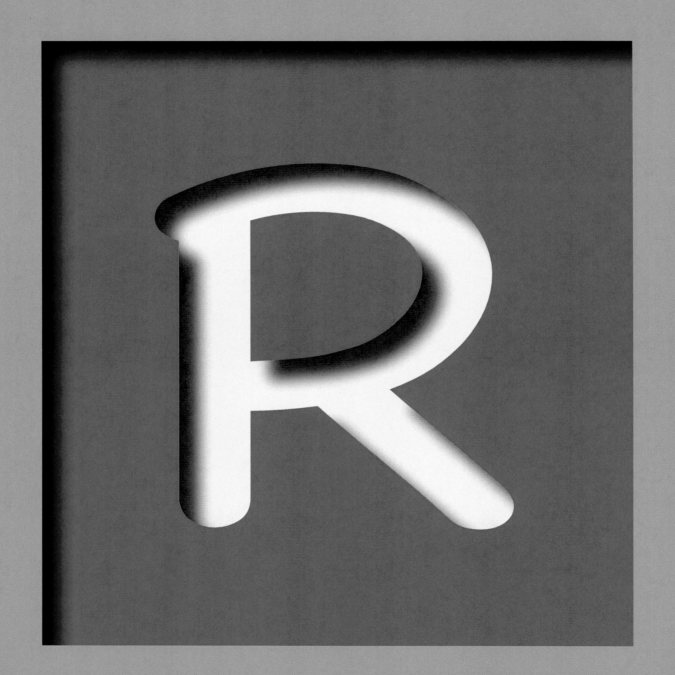

R is for Ruler

S is for son

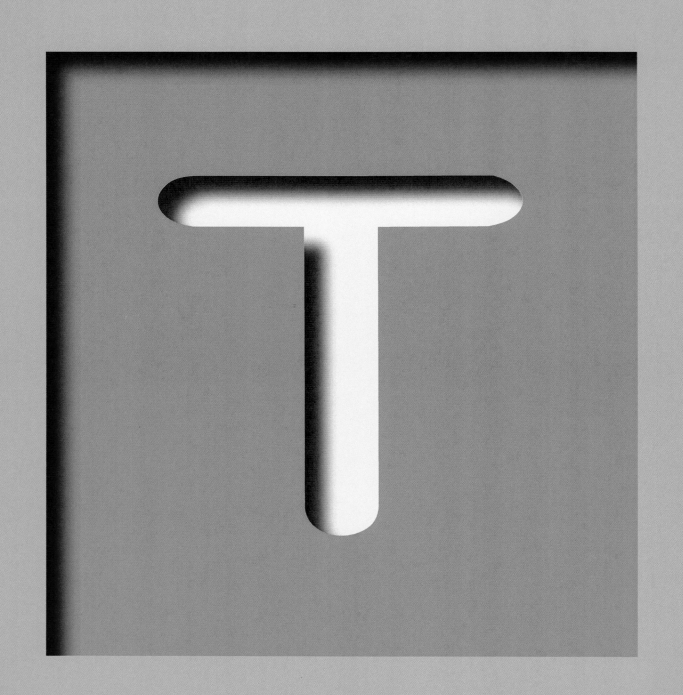

T is for Top

U is for US

W is for Wave

X is for XOXO

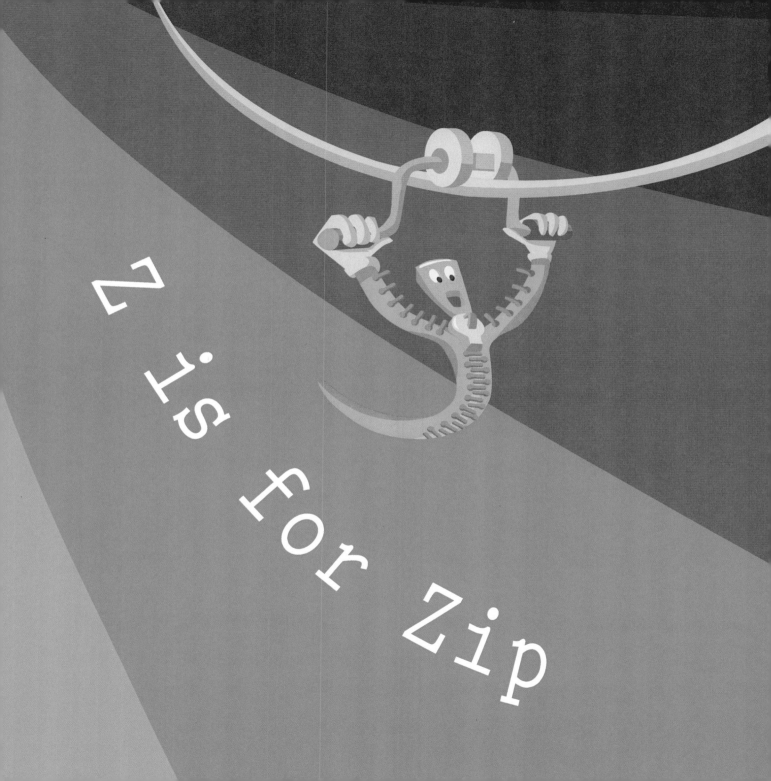

THE
END

THE
END

Ty for taking part in my first book!

I appreciate everybody who has shown me support
through the years, especially my family, my friends,
and now you!

Please follow all my updates under:
@JayKimBooks
You can find my books on Amazon or Kindle.

Alright, I'm trying to keep cool...
But I am genuinely so excited that this is finished.
I really hope you and your loved ones enjoyed this book.

Thank you.

J

Made in the USA
Las Vegas, NV
19 October 2022

57762681R00040